MISCELLANEOUS LINES

To the little ones

Miscellaneous Lines

HARRY GOULBOURNE

Oxford Publishing Services

Published in 2021 by

Oxford Publishing Services
34 Warnborough Road
Oxford, OX2 6JA
www.oxfordpublishingservices.com

ISBN: 978 0 9955278 6 7

Typeset in Berkeley Oldstyle by Oxford Publishing Services.

Cover image by Carla George.

Contents

PART TWO

Preface

These *Lines* were written as a result of the many happy conversations mainly with our first grandchild, Master Bwoy, and looking so much forward to many more conversations which will include our baby granddaughters as they grow and we talk some more.

Acknowledgements

I wish to thank the many friends who at one time or another commented on some of the *Lines* and gave encouragement. I am particularly indebted to Selina Goulbourne, Rachel Wenban Cable, Debbo, Master Bwoy, and Boogieman. Especial thanks to Carla George. As always, I am grateful to Jason and Selina Cohen for making this presentable.

PART ONE

for the boys and girls now, for today

By way of introduction

Our dear little Lapin

Over the past year, I've been meaning to write to you to let you have a sense of how happy your grandmother and I are to have you as our first grandchild. Of course, we are looking forward to many more. On each occasion that I've sat down to write, I've set aside the task because I convinced myself that there's always tomorrow. Such procrastination comes of a long life, about which I'll speak to you over the years – God willing. Moreover, I have been telling myself that it is far more meaningful and practical to come and see you, spend time with you, watch you grow up basking in the love of your parents and your Granny and Grandpa; also us, your Granma, your Grandad.

I hope you'll understand why it's taken so long to come to this task. This is the first letter I'm writing to my first grandchild, and I've been nervous about how to start and which of the many things I want to say to you to say now and what to leave for other occasions.

Of course, for me the delay in writing does not seem so very long. After all, I was in the sixty-second year of my age (as Suetonius or Gibbon would say) when we had the good news from your parents about your imminent arrival. You then had something like eight months before making your physical, visible, and tactile appearance, when we could see you and feel you separately from your mother. I embarked on my sixty-third year a month before your mother brought you into this world, when she and your father began the counting of your life – a counting that with time you'll take over from them as part of the eternal course of being.

So, you see, the delay of just over a year to send you this letter can be neither here nor there for either of us: for me a year is but some weeks; for you it's no doubt an eternity that will last so long you won't ever remember it. You should know, however, that for your parents and for your grandparents, for your uncles and aunties, cousins who are older than you, for people to whom you're related as well as for friends of your parents (many of whom will be more important to you than will be some of your blood-relations), your first year has been momentous. For these folk, your first year will be long remembered.

There are many reasons for this. In due course of time, I hope we'll be able to discuss some of these reasons. Suffice to say that for some of the people around you, your first year has been a year of decision about their own futures, and your entry into their lives offered a moment to pause and take thought. The directions to be taken, the routes to be avoided, and what's to be affirmed about their lives will be emotionally wrapped up with your coming to us. Watching your mother and father and pondering over the beauty of the miracle they've wrought, family-formation will beckon. You do not yet know and will never know how the rapid, awkward and therefore nearly always incoherent early movements of your arms and legs, uncontrollable huge head standing on a narrow plinth of neck, the strange gurgles you make in your throat, and the shouts of 'Heh! Heh!' you uttered from your earliest months resonated with the hopes of those around you.

But, truth be told, there'll be a few – for whom your seemingly irrational cries for your mother's milk, for someone to pick you up in their arms and hold you tight so you feel warm, secure, loved; the cry to let the world or anyone who is close by know that your nappy is wet or sticky and needs to be changed – who will turn up their noses or cast their eyes down or away, and they will think, 'this is not for me!'. Happily, you'll not know this.

And, even more happily, many of this miserable bunch will change their minds as they see you at the beginning of your second year helping your mother sweep the kitchen floor but creating more mess), because you're dissatisfied with her own efforts; as you try to show your father how to improve on his attempts at gardening and house-building.

I've seen your enquiring yet knowing eyes; I've seen and shared with your grandmother your definitive assessments of how business around you is run! Your parents' amateurish ways of doing things will continue to be brushed aside by the certitude you'll bring to bear on their lives. But with time you'll sometimes compromise with them and will concede that perhaps some of the strange ways in which they set about things were OK; but you'll not easily make such concessions in the second year of your age on which you embarked last month, in November 2012 – a day after the celebration of the Armistice. So, you'll be a man of peace.

You may wonder how I know about these things: well, your grandmother and I have seen the pictures supplied by your parents, particularly by your mother who is more than an attentive observer of your growth – she's a veritably *keen* (as Chaucer used this word in the early history of the formation of the language we speak and of which you'll become a master) observer of your progress. You'll see this for yourself in later years.

We've also listened to you communicating with yourself, with the trees, the wind, air, and other elements around you. These are new to you, and you're enjoying the miracle of which you are part – life!

To borrow from the great Robert Nesta Marley, there's 'so much more to say right now, so much more to say…', but your grandmother is calling me to some duty or other. And when I hear from you there're a few additional points I'd like to bring to your attention.

So, for now, 'walk good', as some of your forebears in the high mountains of Clarendon would say, and Godspeed in your wondrous growth.

Your grandmother says 'hello, Sweetie Pie', and that she'll be writing soon.

Our love.

Your ninth birthday

This is the last of your single digit years
You're nine: enjoy it
Next you'll be double digital
You'll begin to notice new things:
Stronger voice, a bigger bwoy
You'll begin to bodily broaden like Daddy
You'll be coming up to Mummy's height
But remember: you will always be your
    Granma's Sweetie Pie.

Continue to ride and run, climb and have
    fun
Enjoy your time with friends
Joyously the years stretch out before you;
    next time you'll be ten
And we'll talk of other things then.

Today in Thanet

Today in Thanet the weather is generous to us:
Rain – mind you very slight – came to us early
    in the morning light
And the birds sung their songs in languages
    unknown to us
But sweet music to our stiffen, our partly
    blocked ears

They try and try to tell us the stories of their
    night, that much we understood
But found us deaf, dumb, inarticulate; no songs
    of our own, just silent sounds and shaking
    of the heads; twisting, pursing of the lips;
    squeezing of the eyelids: questioning

They too have pondered, and still they
    lingered, wondering about us humans
Then, said them all in chirping, musical
    sounds:
Big beasts stumbling as they awake across
    our land to morning light

So, we must whisper
Too few senses do these humans have: they
    hear, they see, sometimes feel and are
    capable of smelling
They even taste the bitterness that
    sometimes comes with daily life;
Sometimes they yawn, expelling the air of
    the hours of their night

Sometimes as humans they think:
We're one, we're human, people, and
    cousins gathered with the living species:
Animals of the field and domestic ones too,
    birds of the skies, fishes of the seas
Sometimes good viruses cry out to say,
    'remember us good ones who help you to
    live'

They, like we, are a universe of Beings
Burst, burst upon the greater Void
And we're here together on our peninsular
Thanet waiting to welcome you.

Our friend Jerry

Since last we spoke and exchanged thoughts
    about our friend Jerry
I must tell you, he came to me mystic like,
    and asked of you:
How, he asked, is the bwoy doing?
    Is he still a bwoy like me?
I'm about to become a man: I'll be twelve years
    old soon, and almost as old as Daddie
I'll almost be as tall as Mammie
Soon, you might not recognize me:
Long arms and legs, stout thighs, nose
    broaden, pushed out mouth
I feel my ears are getting bigger, my hair is
    definitely thicker and stronger
An air of coming teenage membership in
    preparation for manhood, at last
And I'll have to say to you and Granma too:
See me, I'm me, I'm Jerry! So Jerry told me

As well you know, I'm not Jerry's Grandad
Jerry does not have a Granma as you have

Jerry is a poor boy, as well you know
So, we must think of Jerry and what to do
for him.

When Jerry went shopping

Have you still not heard about our dear
      friend, Jerry?
Of his most recent experience?
I can tell you what little has come my
      way:

Growing stronger and wiser; more
      responsible
His parents allowed Jerry to do a little
      shopping at M&S
He needed new underpants

'And how can I help you, young Sir?',
      the attendant asked
'I need new underpants' said Jerry
Pointing along a row of underpants,
      the attendant said,
'Very good, Sir, and all these are satin;
      it's our satin line'

'Oh!' Said Jerry, looking around
'Thank you, but I want new underpants!',
    Jerry responded, a question in his
    eyes.

Who told you so?

Who told you so? I said
That I don't like to stay at other people's
    houses?
Who told you so, inviting mischief?

I love other people's houses:
I walk about, up and down, and round about
Other people's houses!
Once I was watched, quietly, to be sure
There were bedrooms, there were paintings
    and sculptures too
I looked through the bathroom window
I viewed the mango trees; I envied their
    avocados, dwarfed coconut trees,
    abundant and strong coloured flowers:
    bougainvilleas, roses, and hibiscuses
    (shoe-black we used for ink in our
    Clarendon mountain school).

A senior, flamboyant, minister of
    government, master of his house and of
    the prime minister's 'daughter'

Beckoned with the twitch of his index finger
Beckoned to his veranda: 'Another rum?'
Was I a spy looking through his house to
    talk to 'the Opposition?'
He did not ask, but the wrinkle on his
    forehead told me that I knew his question
    right enough!
Looking through a house is a serious matter

When I come to your house and look around
I keep my flat African nose straight as any
    English gentleman would do
My lips compressed, a little fattened, puffed-
    up, for doing so:
Nose, eyes, ears loved your wooden floors,
    your chosen colours, your fridge and
    your pantry and cooker too.

So, you see, I must like your house, I must
    like to stay:
Our dear hostess offers us wine and we
    share some jokes
Of these little things our lives are stitched,
    woven into something whole

And our bed is made. An exception is made
    to see TV; hear the radio. Quietly, mind
    you!

You know how I love other people's houses;
    to be taken around
And our favourite grandson (our only
    grandson) takes his Grandma's hand and
    says
'Grandad. Come, let me show you our
    garden:
The colours Daddy and I have done since
    you were last around'.

Your forthcoming visit

We'll go down to the sea together;
 to Viking Bay, to Joss Bay too
When you visit
And we expect you soon
When you can tell us of your sojourn onto
 and around and into Wordsworth's Lakes
Of Old Man Michael and his faithful,
 comforting, companion, his dear wife
Mother of their bwoy
Bwoy, sadly lost for leaving the Lakes for the
 big city
Mother and Michael had only heard of the
 wandering, lost, in the deep of the town.

You sometimes ask me what I've been doing:
You once surmised, correctly, that I was
 walking 'up and down the house',
 but I'm not yet Polonius.
I've been re-reading Homer, and Daddy told
 me you've been introducing yourself to
 the gods:

Zeus and his father Cronos; brothers and
    sons and daughters:
Poseidon, Athene of the twinkling eyes and
    all the others

And their changing of names when they
    went to Rome: Jupiter, Neptune, Juno
    and all the others
So, when you come into Kent again we'll
    speak again, read again of the gods of
    Greece and Rome
They'll entertain us; we shall humour them
And in their confidence and assurance of
    eternity, they'll gently smile
And ask, 'what is the name of that bwoy
    with the kind and happy laughter?

Being at M&S

How wonderful it was to see you on Sunday
    and share joyous moments
You, Mummy and Daddy; Granma, me
Granma was so happy. Instilled with joy she
    just smiled
She said little, but looked upon your
    growth, your helpfulness, your care for
    all of us
'Granddad', you offered, 'let me open your
    cup of soup for you'
Nimble fingers, able hands

Sadly: I forgot the joke I'd prepared for you,
    but I made Mummy laugh with a poor
    joke for a senior educator
But it's one-thirty morning time so we'll talk
    some more, tomorrow.

I'm back on the page, so let me send you
    these lines that you began as we sat by
    the Deutsch Gym and weeks later had a

poor lunch under the cover of good
service
'Your card is accepted. Do you want a
receipt? Said the voice
Do you want a receipt?
Your card is accepted.
M&S welcome your custom.

Please come again; we'll give you a receipt
Your card is accepted. Do you want a
receipt?
Sainsbury. They imitate us
Not so Tesco. Aldi, ASDA, are not like us
We accept your card, and we can give you
your receipt.

When next you come, we'll accept your card
And give you your receipt.
Receipt and card, card and receipt
You'll always get these at M&S.

Message to you from M&S.
We saw you when you came to us
M&S St Pancras on Sunday afternoon

We were prepared for you; we knew you
    were coming
You came before: Granma and Grandad too.
Your card is accepted, and we have your
    receipt
We still have your receipt and please take
    your card
But come again: we'll accept your card and
    offer you your own receipt.

Would you like your receipt; we like your
    card

This message comes to you from M&S. We
    welcome your custom.

Looking at a flat

This afternoon, Friday, St George's day
Granma and I walked; taking the long, quiet
    road. Slowly, mind
To view a flat overlooking the sea and the
    steps next to Joss Bay
Joss, famous, rich, jovial pirate as you will
    recall.
The accommodation, the gardens,
    particularly the long, wide balcony gave
    us a view across the sea.

All quiet, now.

'But when the white horses come, and when
    the waves lash the coast, we look in
    wonder. Safely from this point. This
    balcony'. She smiles; he smiles too.
    Comfortable mistress and the master of
    these commanding heights.

This is North Foreland Road, and the steps
  leading to western bays are our particular
  liking along this way:
Broadstairs, Viking Bay, Louisa, Dumpton
  too; Ramsgate and the landing points of
  Roman, Saxon, Angles and Jutes,
  Christian too, conquerors all along the
  dipping western coast.

And, all the time and along the way, the
  Seagulls called and complained:
No fisherman's boat close to coast today; no
  fish to throw about for us to feed
But, still we'll fly above, and we'll ask:
Where is your bwoy? Where are your
  granddaughters?

Then, expertly they landed one by one
  folding in their wings
Mighty lords and ladies of the land proudly
  walking just ahead of us,
A strong and musical voice came:
'Masters, mistresses we are of these coasts
And we've come to see you on your way'

And, with pride, spreading their wings again
    to make long coats
Commanded:
'Now, feed us and let us go about our
    business in the town

An early morning

Today, I rose early, again
I was being called by songs from the trees
My friends, the birds had come

Pulling apart the curtains, letting in the light
    of day
I saw them
They bowed and tipped their wings, bidding
    them to stay still
'Good morning, sir; good morning to you',
    they said, and turned their heads
First to right, then to the left, and
    straightened again, feathers keeping still
Eyes set directly on me.
They wanted to hear what I had to say.
What could I do? I nodded, smiled and
    was thankful for their greeting of a new
    day.
I could not sing to them, and they knew
    this, but still they turned their heads in
    sympathy

But when I opened the door, they accepted
this, my welcome to them
Then, in their groups, in their tribes,
according to their own kind
They landed on the lawn in ordered
formations. One by one these groups
came
I could not see what they found for
breakfast, but eating they were
Happy they were
And looked at me seemingly for my
approval or my sighting of them.

Again, I smiled
And bowing their heads they ate from the
ground and the flowers from the trees.
Contentedly so
And, I was happy too.

Poesy for the day

Now, so long troubled as we are, and tearful
    for friends, for family
Neighbours too
Remember: there have been such times
    before and will be again
For so we are, and so we make our lives, our
    world, and feel the pain.
But listen
In the mornings, hear the birds: they
    observe you and sing for you
Their children sing with them, some notes
    discordant, some wings flop too low
Some too high
Only the very old are kept at home, out of
    the way
But keeping the hearth warm, safe for the
    late morning return
And, when they talk amongst themselves we
    hear them singing for us
sharing their poetry
Like you and me they also whistle

But more in tune than you and me, and
  Daddy too
Then they fly away because breakfast is
  served
To eat, to shelter, to be ready for another
  day.

When last you journeyed the long road into our county Kent

You graced us with your presence
You brought us precious presents: salt cod
    fish, not available on our costal
    Broadstairs
Even though our *Fruits des Mer* – a short
    walk from St Peter's – provide us with
    abundance:
Fresh, local, healthy catches
All manner of fins, claws, clotted feet: all
    anchoring, enhancing, tastes of our
    wonderful coasts
The blessings of these isles.

You brought us ackees too:
Encouraging us to seek for ourselves green
    bananas and okras, bold fresh tomatoes
    and sharp onions

You hinted: draw on, select from,
the myriad of spices and bring into the
    melting pot not only Jamaica
What of India and Turkey, of Iran and
    Egypt: you knew you did not need to
    remind of France nor the abundance of
    our England. All these are to our delight
    tonight.

But how much greater was our joy that you
    collected, organized, and brought along
    your bwoys:
The Master Bwoy gathered within and ready
    to give:
Endowing, spreading, happiness.
Gardening, car-driving while staying still;
    teasing Daddy
And, closing the evening: making us judges
    of 'dancing with Mummy'.

All these presents you brought and we are
    thankful.

A noise in the
light of day

Here's a story I must tell you:
I was in our kitchen watching and listening
    to the news of the day
Then: a sharp sound from the middle floor
It was your Granma.
Still in my dressing-gown, still half-awake –
    I rushed to our middle-floor.
Trembling, but of strong mind and presence
    she said 'we're invaded! Fast, fast!'
'Invaded? I asked. 'How so?'
The Norsemen, the Danes, the Normans no
    longer land at Broadstairs or along our
    coasts
'The house is taken over! Come upstairs!
    Quick! Quick!'

Tea spilt; long gown got in the way; but I
    rushed; I got upstairs
No Vikings to be seen

But there were beatings on our windows, there
    were attackers in our house, in our home
We were under siege
I looked out quick; I grabbed one of my
    hard-wood African walking sticks – you
    know I keep them at strategic spots –
There was no one to be seen!

But: by the window in our bedroom a wood
    pigeon sat and looked at me
I rushed away, and in your bedroom another
    looked out the window onto the street
Then , with a turn of the head, looked
    around and asked who I was
I grabbed one of the pillows from your baby-
    bed to protect my face, because they
    started to fly about
I asked, no I told, your Granma to leave the
    room; to go downstairs; to be out of reach
    of the ghastly invaders.
She did not like the smells of these visitors
(You already know: your Granma does not
    like the smells of uninvited visitors such
    as these!)

So, there I was, with little help from
    Hitchcock's birds – all within our home!
    Windham's Triffids flooded my mind. I
    was near panic

I managed to open windows; I managed to
    keep a pillow close. After a while, they
    looked at me;
This time they smiled, tipped their wings,
    and graciously flew to empty space,
    refreshing air. They did not say goodbye;
    just the flapping of wings.

Rabbit Hill

Beauty. Unexpectedly visiting
She comes back in our gardens, the trees,
    and over our roof
She comes as snow and with winks;
    a provocative smile on her cheeky
    face
Wonderment is our response, but we smile
    too and bid her welcome.
I've come, she said, to take away any
    sadness of Summer past
And greyness too, and make some
    merriments part of our play:
So, dance, jump and prance about;
    like my dog, the eternal friend
Frolic: roll, show your paws, hang your
    tongue, open your ears
And know that you're again in heaven,
    again and again. And, know this:
Your favourite grandson is a happy bwoy in
    London town.

In the middle of the night, when all is dark,
    mysterious
When likkle bwoys, likkle girls
Enjoy the silence
And silence descends, rolling down from the
    top
From the hill that we call the hill of the
    family Rabbit
Today, there is no thunder, there is no rain
Yet, the place is damp and wet
And all around us the houses, the driveways,
    the walls are white
And silence bids us quiet
Open your ears to today's music.

I cried for my Mummy, I cried for my Daddy
    too
But out, out, to the woods they ran, calling
    and beckoning to me
We ran and we ran, and the silence became
    abundant; loud
And the more we ran.

An open field welcomed us:

We embraced:

Grass; a meadow, gentle grazing horses;
    goats in the distance, dancing Billies
    making mischief: I awoke. And along the
    lake Mummy, Daddy, Mr Rabbit

And I looked out across a peaceful park.

And we added it all to the tale built of
    London Town.

Today's joke

Here is a tale you must've heard a version of:

Two mice holding each other in their hole
Listening, listening to the sound of the cat
    outside, saying 'meow', 'meow'
'We must wait, it's our main enemy waiting
    to eat us', said one to the other
'Yes, we will wait', second mouse agreed
'Meow, meow' came louder to the entrance
    and the two mice moved back
Deeper and deeper into their narrowing
    hole.

A long silence followed; there was a linger-
    ing; time stood still. Not a sound from
    without.

Then: 'Rough, rough, rough' came a bark;
    'rough, rough!' An angry growling sound.
    A long silence followed by a satisfied,
    happy, dog.

'Let's get out of here: the dog is not our
enemy', said one mouse to the other
And, out they jumped: the first one was
quickly eaten; the second was trapped
But also soon eaten!

Later, the cat laid on its back, feet crossed.
What relaxation!
Digesting lunch: 'Ah, the happiness of this
life:
'My teachers were right! I always found it
useful to speak more than one language.
Amen, dear Lord. And cheers to our
teachers too!'

The tides of Viking Bay

The tides are here and are turning;
tides do:
Uncaring, no discrimination, no preference,
no hate
But merciless
The music is rhythmic
But there is no dancing, no jumping, no
prancing

Close your eyes and your mind
Close down your thoughts
Now: listen to the rhythm of your body, the
quiet beating of your heart

Hear and feel the beauty of your soul beside
the flow, the movement, of the sea.

Fragments of a telephone conversation

You're back at school

So your Granma and me were told

Mummy too is back at school I hear for time
tables and things must be sorted

Daddy has never been away from school has
he Grandad?

Not since the age of twenty-three months

And, an NHS man, I suppose he must stay in
the front line, as at school.

He cycles to his spot, but it is now closer
home

No longer inhaling dust and smoke; the
pollution, yak!

Away from our foxes on Rabbit Hill, he
pumps his way to Croydon

No longer riding to Guys, riding to Tommy,
and sometimes to Kings as well

Mummy too stands on the front line, her
guidance is needed

She never entirely left her school, she would
    never leave the children
Even at home Mummy is always at her
    school
But we read to each other and we cook;
    together, you understand
Daddy too, sometimes; sometimes all the
    time
And with Mummy (and Daddy too
    sometimes) we do maths and English
Mummy wants me to love geography; she is
    a geographer, not a philosopher (so she
    told me)
With Daddy it's music and chess as well
And always the garden and the allotment:
    I've planted my own vegetables,
    everywhere
When we come to see you soon after the
    Covid 2020
Granma and I will help you in the garden
But, Grandad, you must admit, Grandad:
Granma and I always do all the hard work;
You just stay in the kitchen, cooking, and
    cooking.

You are right, because you're our favourite
grandson
Grandad, grandad, you have only one
grandson!
I know you're likely to be so:
And growing boy, you'll become venturous
youth, kind man, strong
Enquiring mind, observant eyes: set upon
the world into which you go forth.

The year's long day

Today is the longest day of the year, if just
    by seconds
but also by light, by air and sounds from
    outside your door.
So, look out and listen to the sounds around
    you.
Smell and feel the air; try to touch it!
Record in your memory for your treasure
    chest of life:
Immaterial, measure-less, weightless
But these will always connect across space,
    across time
With Mummy and Daddy, Grandpa and
    Granny. Your Granma and Grandad too
Your cousins across our spherical, not yet
    rounded, world.

Our beloved wisteria

Our wisteria's first flowering of the year is
gone and the leaves are out
But we still have the visit of our favourite
Bumblebee
Bless her
She comes in the morning and she says hello
in buzzing sounds,
making music
By her colourful wings she says to us: 'happy
morning'
And from day to day she asks:
How are your granddaughters today?

Dressed for the morning

Ascending the stairs, at the fifth step I saw you
Sitting as if in state
And you winked as if expecting me; you
    smiled
With widened lips and marbled eyes
Your Napoleon hat tipped to the left, not at
    me
Your black suit, red bow-tie, mocking blue-
    suede shoes
No anger on your face.
Calm and collected; serene.
Benignly you said to me:

'I'm your friend: I sit on the step of your
    favourite grandson's favoured step!
I shall jump as your only grandson used to
    jump; but not on you
You will not need to catch me, and my name
    is not Lapin!
I'm not even your son with his pants over
    his trousers. Superman!

I come without his cape. I have not
destroyed my Mummy's dresses and her
curtains are all intact.
So. Tell me a story so I can go away and one
day tell my daughters and my sons that I
saw you and you looked into my face:
and your eyes were bright; you had no
fear

You were not scared of my long black
swishing, waving tail
My many toes on my foursome feet were of
no account to you
In appreciation, in happiness, my whiskers
freely twitched.
I tipped my hat

And we smiled.

In the garden reading some of our favourites

You heard, you saw, how happy the birds
    were today on your short visit.
They were glad to see you. They continue to
    tell me so.
They'd waited for your coming to their
    garden; they knew you'd come; they
    too had missed you and the joy you
    bring
They were glad that you took along your
    Daddy, and in conversation, you talked of
    your Mummy
You talked of your Granny and Granpa too
But, today: it was your Daddy and you; your
    Granma and me

As usual you exercised the sliding door to
    your castle – our guest house:
Friends, family, entertainment; joyous times
    there

In the garden we read from Keats, and you
should never keep too long from him
One day you'll know of his times (of slavery
and wealth; privilege and travels; protests
and struggles too)
Of his friend Byron, but especially one
Byshee who answered to Percy and
Shelley and wrote great poems,
particularly of freedom

Now, you may twiggle and turn on your bed
(it's your right to do so) as your Mummy
or Daddy explain
But, you must never forget to read aloud for
yourself and your friends
Develop your strengthen, your memory,
your knowledge expand let it expand to
encompass the world
And one day relate, inform and deliver your
gift to your daughters and your sons.

Our Master Robin Redbreast

I'm back to my habit of old:
I wake too early, have my mug of black
    unsugared tea
I see the day come awake
And Master Robin Redbreast descends and
    dances on the lawn
Then comes to the window, not twitting, not
    smiling
But in his own way, by movements of head,
    relaxed shoulders
Clearly said: 'Good morrow to you too, Sir!'

Your car awaits you

Your Granma and I must tell you:
Your car of vintage years
Fully oiled, fuelled, ready to drive by you
    alone
One arm on the top, one arm and two feet
    dragged on the wooden floor
Sits stably parked by the rug
Hand made by a woman and her man in the
    high mountains of Turkey
Your car waits your coming.

Morning opening

The opening of the morning, what a
    beautiful thing to feel and behold:
Light creeps upon the darkness
Trees reclaim their seasonal colours
While flowers await the slower coming of
    the sun.
The last moments of quietness, tranquillity
Peacefulness of the dark night
And, then the birds of England talk amongst
    themselves
Not knowing they sing for all of us.

Garden pruning

This year the gardeners came later than
    expected
They shaped the trees, and limited the
    upward growth
Spaces are now opened for the fattening of
    each plant
For the flowers to show their beauty
For the birds to spread their wings, sing,
    whisper
And sometimes they look at us, questioning
    us
With the turns of their heads, their changing
    colours
Questioning our silence!

But I think they're looking for you:
To see your dripping nose, whisper to you,
    commune
As only birds, children, squirrels, rabbits can
    do.

Dogs can be jealous; cats can scratch and
spit with anger

Lizards, all creepy things who cannot even
sing

But some can sting and bite! And, how well
they know it

But you and Granma, and sometimes me,
can sit and see, and think of how to
understand.

Unentitled

I saw you walking
Up and down the restaurant holding hands
You were talking to your uncle.
Later, I said to you 'your uncle is a funny
    man!'

You shook your head
And, after time and thought, you said,
    correcting me
'No! He's a nice man, a very nice man
And he's *my* uncle, not yours!'

PART TWO

for the women and men of tomorrow

Our Co-Op village
St Peter's staff

Just to say thank you to the staff of Co-Op
    St Peter's
You've kept us provisioned in these troubled
    times of Covid-19
Courteous and helpful, you smile and ask
'How are you'; 'anything else?'
You point to what we often require
We're grateful.
We enclose a card of our grandson Lapin
When he was 7 (a growing artist)
In earlier years he rolled on your floor in the
    way of customers, and asked about Tara.

We all look forward to a great year 2021
When Covid-19 will be brought to the
    ground!

Back to school today?

When I rang you this morning before your
    breakfast time
There was ringing and ringing, then silence
I rang again and heard 'Hello'
The voice was not boy, nor girl's; not man or
    woman's:
The voice said: The Master is not here, he's
    at school today
Call again at eventide
I'm alone; first time in six months since
    Covid came.
And, you are? Don't tell me: you're Monkey,
    are you not?
I'm not Monkey! I'm Mister Monkey
I walk on two legs just like you
Master ate two of my legs, he liked them so
Monkey ran away some days ago saying:
I like my four legs, and you shall not have
    them
Master Bwoy shall have only Mister
    Monkey

I'm not allowed in Master's class, I cannot
    stand alone in the playground
But here I'm in his bedroom, ears intact, but
    two legs gone;
Yet, today, today I'm Master and I'm at my
    own school
Meanwhile Master Bwoy romps, jumps and
    prances on the fields of DPS
With friends and with teachers, they're
    covering Covid in 19 steps.

Your loss,
our loss

Nev, dear bwoy these are troubled times
Times that our mothers and fathers, our
    forebears foresaw and managed.
Now, it's our time.

I have a vague memory of Miss Clem's
    birth
Your beautiful mother, my aunt Emilie, the
    breast-feeding of the newcomer into our
    narrow world
Like you, me was a likkle bwoy, and we
    looked on from partly closed doors
Something special was happening that me
    didn't understand, just awed
No explanation; smiles aplenty
But there was a whole heap ah talk among
    the big people dem.
We likkle ones listened; we kept our
    counsel; our silence.

We were happy: a new life had come among
    us; though mysterious
Things happening, brightening our quiet,
    mountainous hills.

Now she is gone
But so many years have passed and we were
    blessed by her time with us.

Oscar I always remember as an awkward
    bwoy, obedient to his grandmother
A kind, perhaps too silent a bwoy; he grew
    to be a kindly man, as I saw him
Alas, I didn't know him well
He lived on the edge of the wider family, sad
    to say.
Always wanted to cut, collect, something
    from the field for us
We were not to go back to Kingston empty-
    handed; without a gift from the land
His farm, his grandmother's land

In this week of the loss of your youngest
    sister, the loss of a nephew

Muster the courage that has always made
you shine!

The Skylakers

These troubled times of Covid-19 aka
    Coronavirus
They linger and linger still, ever breathing;
    never idle
Trouble upon trouble, stealing:
Our cold Winter, our refreshing Spring and
    warm, dry, Summer
Most of all my beloved Autumn.
All these are now gone.
We have lost twenty twenty in the year of
    our Lord, our Common Era

And, in our despair, we have our Tyrants
    spread across the world
Surnamed Evilous:
Trumpus to the right and Xiannus to the
    left, they looked both north and south
    cross-eyed East and West
Putinius looked within and without
Modius said, 'we're many', graviliciously
    digging deep into the heart of his kind
    country

And, all around were spread their followers
Within and without they testified, bearing
    witness to their masters, who said:
I'm Borosono and I'm the Brazil
I'm Vitarte and I'm the Philippines.
And Chorus, who rode beside them, said:
We lead the way for much of Asia, much of
    Africa; South America too.
We are known as Disaster
In Europe we are called Cultivated Chaos
    and our Boritus smiles and grins with
    half-closed, 1950s, Hollywood cow-boy,
    eyes
Together, together, we are the way out of
    blinding light into the new age of
    nothingness.

But, far, far in the sky, up in the firmament
    the flicker of a light few could see.
Fewer could hear the booming sound of
    birth, of life yet to be imagined:

The Skylakers were awakening; laziness was
    bidding goodbye!

Conversations with American friends

Leah, how happy to hear from you
Sabrina alerted me, for first I did not see, did
  not hear from you
Still: I do not hear how our American friends
  receive the moment's trump of time:
Coup or putsch; the push is for dictatorship.
  The 1930s:
No law, no rule; the of rule of law, respect of
  conventions, are gone.

I'm closing now my e-mail for the evening,
but contemplating the events of the day
And I salute you:
you've saved your country from the brink of
  war, and Chaos kept abay.
Not Caligula with his little boots; not Nero
  with his lyre
Could take the streets of Rome, nor could
  roar as loud as Twittering Trump

Not the Athenian Tyrants, who
    frightened our father Herodotus who
    warned
Even though your Founding Fathers
    made provisions, not taken:
Not balances, not proportional
    distributions, not tolerance, not Locke
    or Hobbes, not Jefferson
No Lincoln, no FDR, no JFK nor brother
    Robert
No Johnson, no Carter, no Clinton no
    Obama

Nevertheless, as my father would say:
    on this bright Autumn day in
    November there's a light
And it's not far away
Old of age, and years have passed
Like Simeon he prayed for a new birth
Over the horizon, but after a long walk
A prince, humbly
Strengthened Biden, lately come and
    comes to dumpth the Trump

So, Great Yeats

The coming of the Second Coming striding
    on lion's feet to Bethlehem is no more

We need not fear

Joe and Kamala are doing the crossing of the
    waters.

In the spirit of MacNeice

I've seen MacNeice, and he wished to pray
   with me
He was not yet born
And I was stumbling, rumbling in the womb
He asked me to save him
I asked him to save me
We were not yet born

In the deep recesses of time and space, of
   consciousness,
Nothingness and emptiness
I looked around: emptiness
Space, infinity, endlessness
Everything, and yet nothingness.

I close my eyes but still I see
You and I cannot hear the emptiness of time
   and space
What you see, what you hear, your sense of
   taste and touch are buttered temporal
Temporal you are, temporal you'll be

Oh man of man that you are; and, without
   woman
Half way on your way

Not far from the Broadstairs where you
   landed
You're lost and you have no papers
The seas do not know you
The ships cannot return for you – alone.
   Frightened man, on a waving sea
And your family weep, wondering where
   you are
On the cold northern waves on which, in
   desperation, they cast you.

For Sam Orgias

My dear, dear, Sam, Sam Orgias, friend and
    gentle guide
Just learnt that you've crossed over and left us
We are poorer: your soft humour
mocking, embracing, gentle smile
They are now gone
But your generosity and kindness
The twinkle in your mischievous, loving
    eyes, your beautiful blackness, your
    strong teeth
Understanding of who and what we are
Sometimes a seeming defiance born of West
    African man or Congo man
Sometimes gentle, cultured Grenadian,
    learned French man, and English
    gentleman too
Mathematician, speaker of languages, traveller

Take comfort with the forebears, lay at rest
And in the depth of time and space, know
    that you've left a goodly son

When, a little boy, teased you by calling you
    Mr Orgias
Showing his love, and dismissing you were
    the Ambassador
But you were not only for Grenada; you
    were Caribbean man,
And so, universal man of peace and love
You remain ambassador for all people of
    good will.

Professor Walter Rodney

To be with Walter Rodney were events of
    gladness, warmth and learning
Whether in London or Dar-es-Salaam
Moments of beauty, times of joy never to be
    forgotten.
Youthful, learned, wise, warmth, empathetic
    man and person
Taken down long before his three score
    years and ten
1980, a year of loss: Maas Bob went first in
    that year
They went across the unmerciful seas
    Odysseus never saw
But they shouted last: justice will come.
And as 2020 rings alarms across the world
Time and justice are answering to the bells
    of disappear:
They say: lives matter.

For Joan

Dear, our dear, Joan how we miss you
Words fail us
The edict governing togetherness, bred of
  Covid-19
Deny us passage to honour you today.
We join your family: your Bob, our long-
  time mentor, guide, and friend
Your daughters, their families
The friends who were and are about and
  around you
Together, we honour you.
And still you embrace us, enfold us in the
  depths and at the entry of our
  memories:
With kindness, generosity, relaxed
  conversations over unrushed time.

But these stand above all: your gentleness,
  listening ear
The serenity of your smile, your warmth, the
  quiet grace, your *dignitas.*

The sting of death can take none of these away.

———————◆◆◆◆———————

For Professor
Edwin Jones

We will always miss you;
    and your passing is our great loss:
Of your kindness, of your grace, of your
    dignity
The beauty of your smile,
    your tenderness
The twinkle in your eyes
Your considered advice before we took some
    steps of life walk-ways
How you cared for our students and
    institutions,
Our careers, the welfare of our families
Our well-being,
    our happiness
Our country and heritage; of how strong our
    people have always stood.

And humbly so.

Your generosity had no bounds
Well before these present times of measured,
    calculated giving
You gave
And you carried forth and engendered in us
    (I think of Peter, of Richard, especially
    myself)
The radical tradition of our likkle country;
    of the likkle man
The likkle woman who send into the skies
    our island-land.

Teacher, mentor, friend, you helped us so
You sought no praise, expected no reward.
But Jamaica has lost a great son
I have lost a wise brother
So. Sail safely on …

You have no need of the coin for the
    ferryman.

On our troubled road

I'm on the shore, belched from the belly of
    the whale
I stand on sinking sands, but I'm firm and I
    can see solid rocks
They stand above me
They welcome me to the dry land. They
    asked my name and I say Jonah
But I cannot remember the message from my
    god Yahweh to deliver to you
So, help me
Even refreshed as I am – and thank you –
    alive as I am due to you
I know only one living miracle: I'm alive and
    shall journey on.

But, I must first tell you: as I passed a
    crippled man leaning on his wobbling
    stick, he said to me:
On the left turn of this road – and he
    pointed
You will meet a man

If he stops you, he'll tell you he's on his way
  from Troy, from Priam's town

Remember, never forget, the name
  Odysseus, who will become Ulysses
A cousin of Maas Ananyse – Greek, Roman,
  Ashante, but no matter
Later still to become every troubled traveller
  on the rough, pebbled road, the
  swallowing seas
Not always a whale to safety, no boat to
  help; no darling Circe
Just man, just woman, just a walking stick,
  just road and turbulent deep dividing
  waters and bumps along the way
Troubled roads: Dante will tip his Firenze
  hat and say he's on his way to see his
  beloved; St Paul is on his way to
  salvation; and the Don? Brave knight.
  Well, he's off to save the world.

You must genuflect, think, and say thanks
  for the life you're given.

A bad poem for our bad times

What tearful, what fearful times we share
    with our children and children's
    children
How suddenly the gods have fallen upon us
Not lightning, not bolts, not thunder
Not just storms, wild fires, not angry
    hurricanes
Not just eruptions, not just large scale
    murders.

But there's pestilence
And emptiness spreads our public spaces
Desolation and fear stalk our social spheres
The gods are angry, they cannot contain
    themselves

They come as Putin, they come as Xi, they
    come as Bolsonaro
As the man of the Philippines they come

They come as Boris
They come as one united

And together stump their feet, and with
    pouted lips, they shout in one voice:
My name is Trump.

Covid 2020

So stranded, so cornered as we are
Hope we all for happier days, more blessed
  times
When we'll spill forth onto our streets
When we'll enter our shops, flood our pubs
Our parks, and our playgrounds will
  welcome us

And we shall say: home again
And we shall laugh and tell each other jokes
Welcome, welcome, my home is yours
Invite me to your own, and I'll come
And we'll speak again, and look each other
  in the face

But our eyes will still tell the stories:
Lonely domestic scenes, unseen friends,
  families to touch, families afar
Across the continents, the oceans
The islands of the seas within our
  neighbourhoods.

But we'll not be defeated by that beast with
    many hands
Feet and toes spread apart, pointing to all
    directions of the circled, inter-netted
    world
Bolsonaro, Duterte, Trump
And as trinity answer to the prenomen
    Coronavirus
By deed-poll no longer the number 666, but
    hereafter Covid-2020.

INDEX